Hallelujah

Popular Songs of Inspiration

WISE PUBLICATIONS
part of The Music Sales Group
London/New York/Paris/Sydney/Copenhagen/Berlin/Madrid/Hong Kong/Tokyo

Published by:
Wise Publications
14-15 Berners Street, London W1T 3LJ, UK.

Exclusive Distributors:
Music Sales Limited
Distribution Centre, Newmarket Road, Bury St Edmunds, Suffolk IP33 3YB, UK.
Music Sales Pty Limited
20 Resolution Drive, Caringbah, NSW 2229, Australia.

Order No. AM1000659
ISBN 978-1-84938-557-2
This book © Copyright 2010 Wise Publications,
a division of Music Sales Limited.

*Due to copyright changes, this book, previously published
as AM994323, has been reprinted with revised contents.*

Compiled by Nick Crispin.
Edited by Sam Harrop.

Printed in the EU.

Your Guarantee of Quality
As publishers, we strive to produce every book to the highest
commercial standards.
This book has been carefully designed to minimise awkward page turns
and to make playing from it a real pleasure.
Particular care has been given to specifying acid-free, neutral-sized
paper made from pulps which have not been elemental chlorine bleached.
This pulp is from farmed sustainable forests and was produced with
special regard for the environment.
Throughout, the printing and binding have been planned to ensure
a sturdy, attractive publication which should give years of enjoyment.
If your copy fails to meet our high standards, please inform us
and we will gladly replace it.

www.musicsales.com

Bridge Over Troubled Water

Words & Music by Paul Simon

When you're___ wea-ry___   feel-ing___ small,

2. When you're down and out,___ when you're on the

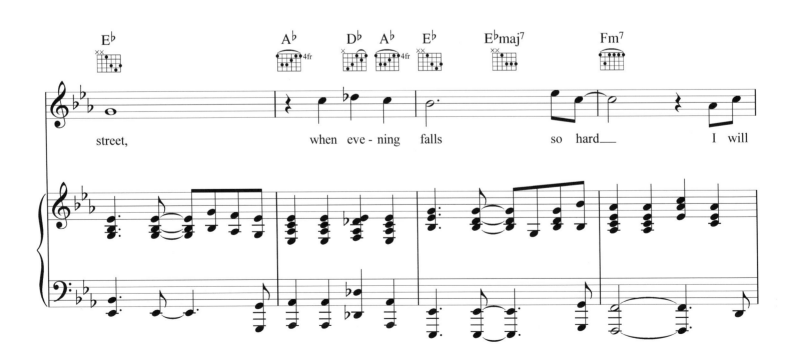

street, when eve - ning falls so hard___ I will

Sail on___ sil - ver girl,___ sail on___ by. Your time has come to shine,___ all your dreams are on their___ way. See how they

like a bridge o - ver trou - bled wa - ter,

I will ease your mind.

Angel

Words & Music by Sarah McLachlan

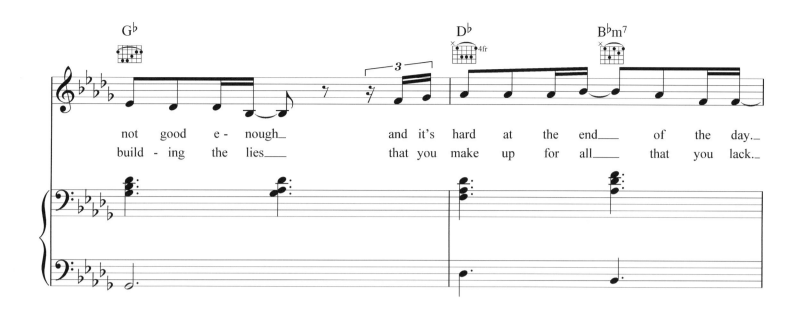

not good e - nough___ and it's hard at the end___ of the day.___
build - ing the lies___ that you make up for all___ that you lack.___

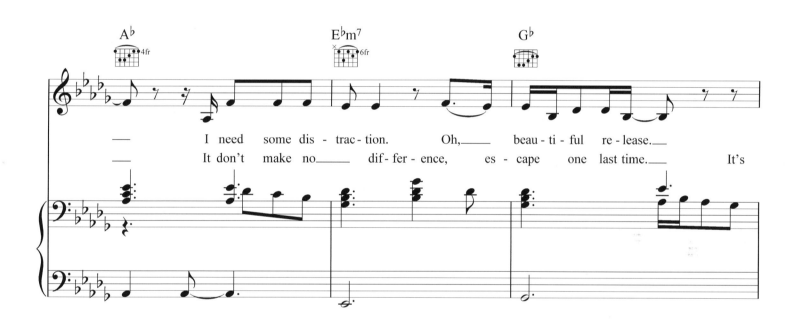

— I need some dis - trac - tion. Oh,___ beau - ti - ful re - lease.___
— It don't make no___ dif - fer - ence, es - cape one last time.___ It's

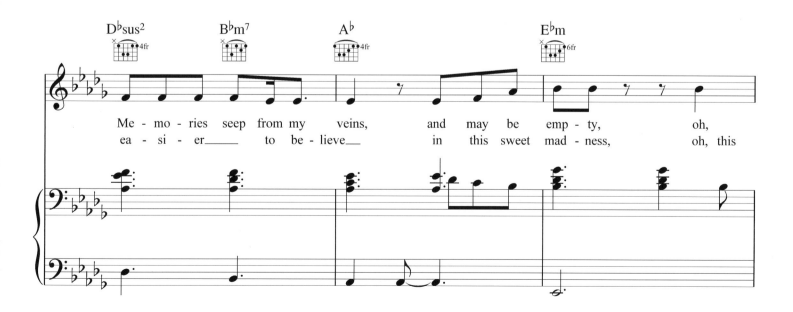

Me - mo - ries seep from my veins, and may be emp - ty, oh,
ea - si - er___ to be - lieve___ in this sweet mad - ness, oh, this

weight-less and may-be I'll find some peace to-night._____ In the

glo - ri - ous sad - ness that brings me to my knees.

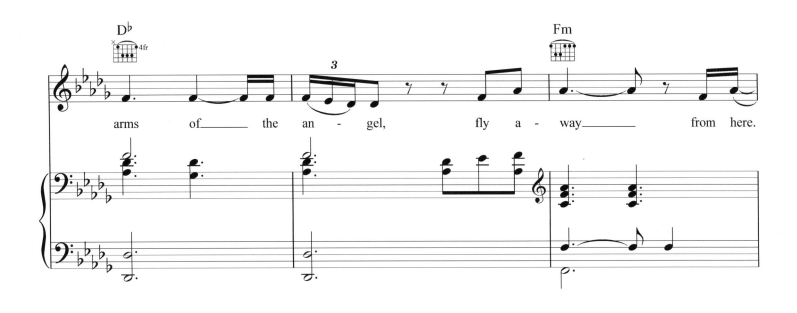

arms of_____ the an - gel, fly a - way_____ from here.

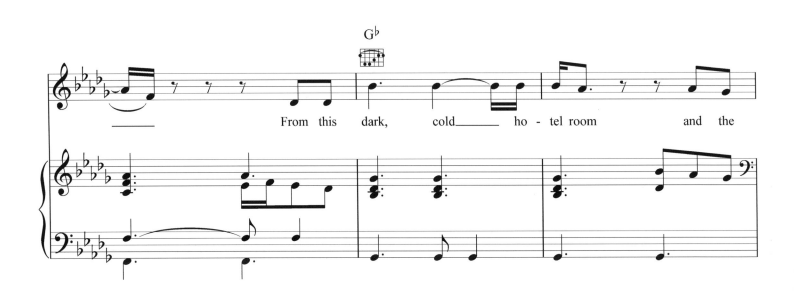

From this dark, cold_____ ho - tel room and the

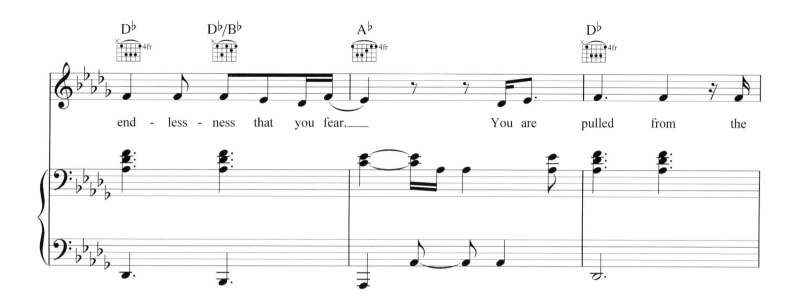

end - less - ness that you fear.___ You are pulled from the

wreck - age of your si - lent___ re - ve - rie.___ You're in the

arms of_____ the an - gel, may you find_____

some com - fort_____ here.

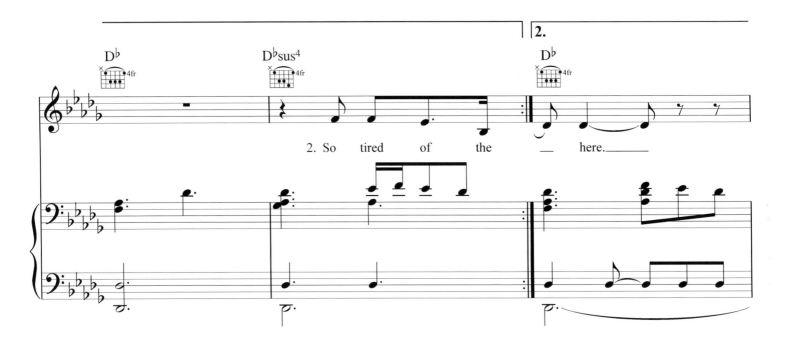

2. So tired of the ___ here._____

You're in the arms of_____ the

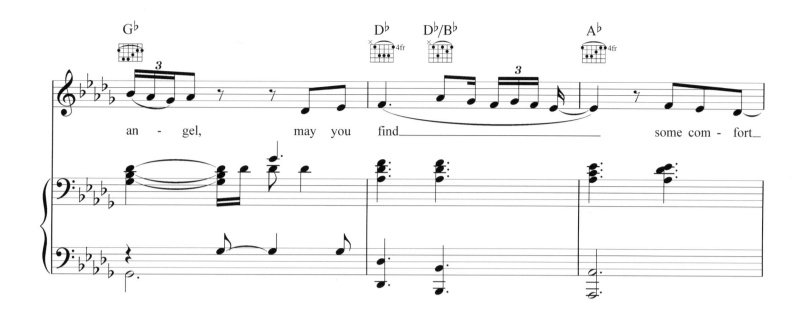

an - gel,   may you find_____   some com - fort__

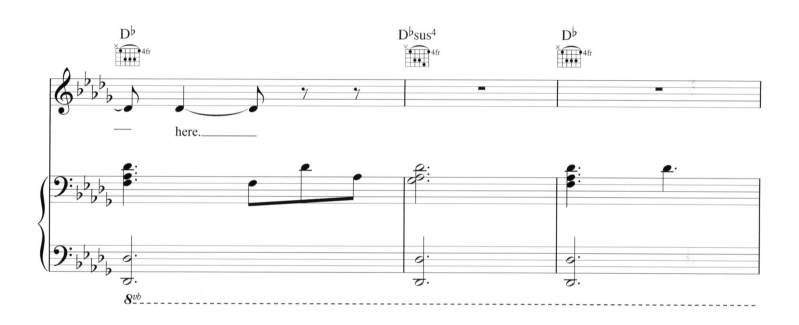

__ here._____

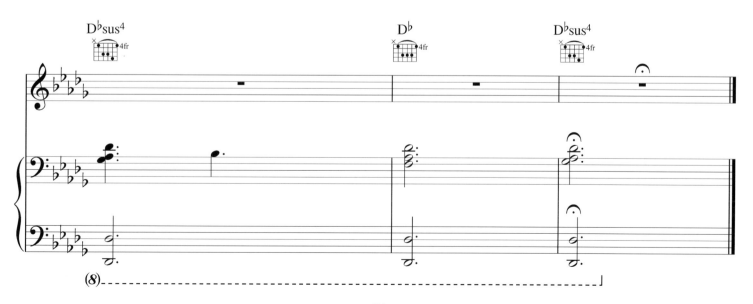

Angels

Words & Music by Robbie Williams & Guy Chambers

When I'm feel-ing weak and my pain__ walks down a one__ way street,

I look a-bove and I know__ I'll al - ways be blessed__

__ with love.__ And as the feel-ing grows she brings

flesh to my bones and when love is dead, I'm lov-ing an - gels in-stead.

Carry On

Words & Music by Jamie Hartman

33

Every Grain Of Sand

Words & Music by Bob Dylan

Fix You

Words & Music by Guy Berryman, Chris Martin, Jon Buckland & Will Champion

Tune guitar down a semitone

♩ = 70

1. When you try___ your best but you don't suc - ceed,___ when you get___

___ what you want but not what you need,___ when you feel___ so tired but you can't sleep,___

stuck in re - verse. _____ 2. And the tears

(2.) __ come stream - ing down your face, _____ when you lose __
(3.) high up a - bove and down be - low, _____ when you're

__ some-thing you can't re - place, ____ or you love __ some-one but it goes to waste, __
too in love to let it go, _____ but if you nev - er try, you'll nev - er know __

__ could it be worse? _____
__ just what you're worth. _____

Lights will guide____ you home____ and ig - nite____ your bones____

____ and I will try____ to fix you.____

3. And

Guitar

cont. sim.

Tears   stream   down   your   face__

when   you lose   some - thing   you   can - not   re - place.__

Footprints In The Sand

Words & Music by Per Magnusson, David Kreuger, Richard Page & Simon Cowell

1. You walked with me,___ foot-prints in the sand___ and
2. I see my life___ flash a-cross the sky;___ so

helped me un-der-stand___ where I'm go — ing.
man-y times___ have I___ been so a - fraid.

45

Gold

Words & Music by Prince

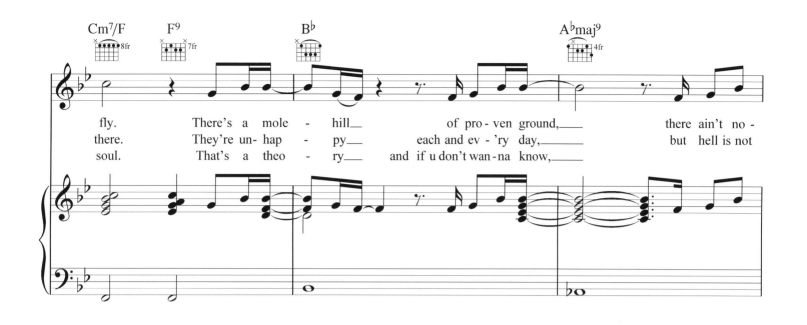

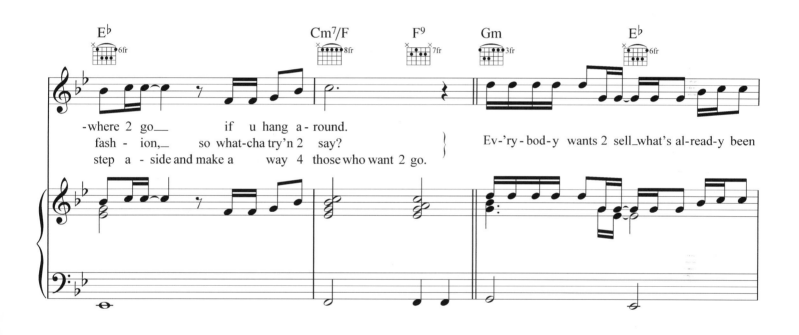

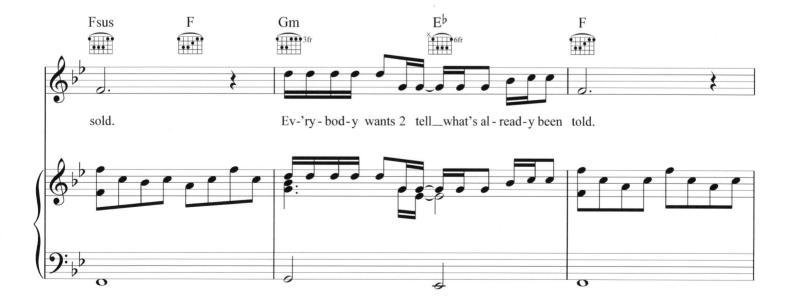

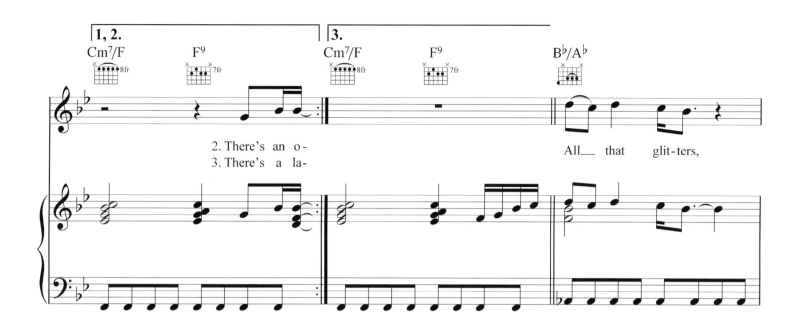

2. There's an o-
3. There's a la-

All___ that glit-ters,

all___ that glit-ters, all___ that glit-ters

ain't gold.

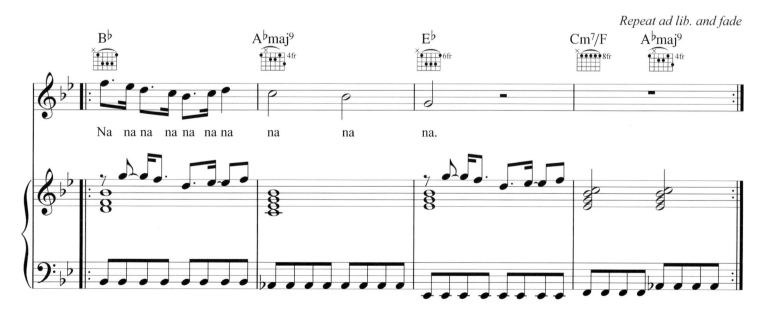

Na na na na na na na na na na.

Repeat ad lib. and fade

Hallelujah

Words & Music by Leonard Cohen

ma - jor lift, the baf - fled king com - pos - ing Hal - le - lu - jah.___
cut your hair, and from your lips she drew the Hal - le - lu - jah.___
vict - 'ry march, it's a cold and it's a brok - en Hal - le - lu - jah.___
mov - ing too and ev - 'ry breath we drew was Hal - le - lu - jah.___

Hal - le - lu - jah, Hal - le - lu - jah, Hal - le -

-lu - jah, Hal - le - lu - - - - jah.

1, 2, 3.

4.

2. Well, your -jah.
3. Well,
4. Well, there

54

Hal - le - lu - jah,   Hal - le - lu - - jah.   Hal - le -
- lu - jah,   Hal - le - lu - jah.   Hal - le - lu - jah,
Hal - le - lu,____   Hal - le - lu - jah.   Hal - le -
- lu - jah.   Hal - le - lu - jah,   Hal - le - lu - jah.

From A Distance

Words & Music by Julie Gold

voice of___ ev - 'ry___ man.
songs of___ ev - 'ry___

2. From a

man. God_ is watch-ing us, God_ is watch-ing us. God_ is

watch-ing us from a dis - tance.

60

ech - oes   through   the   land._____   It's the hope of__ hopes,_____ it's the

love of__ loves,_____ it's the heart_____ of ev - 'ry man.   It's the

hope of__ hopes,_____ it's the love of__ loves,_____ it's the song of____ ev - 'ry__

man.

FRANKIE LAINE

I Believe

Words & Music by Ervin Drake, Irvin Graham, Jimmy Shirl & Al Stillman

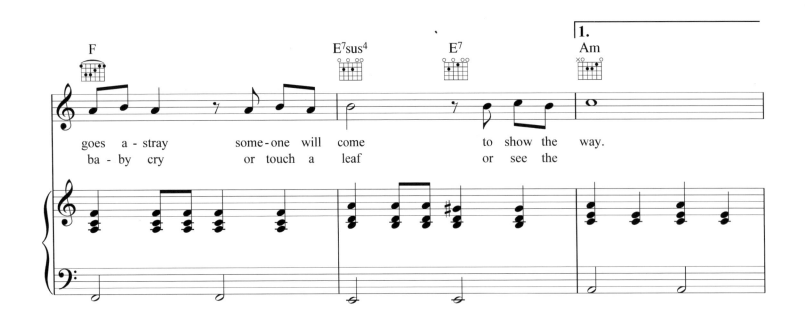

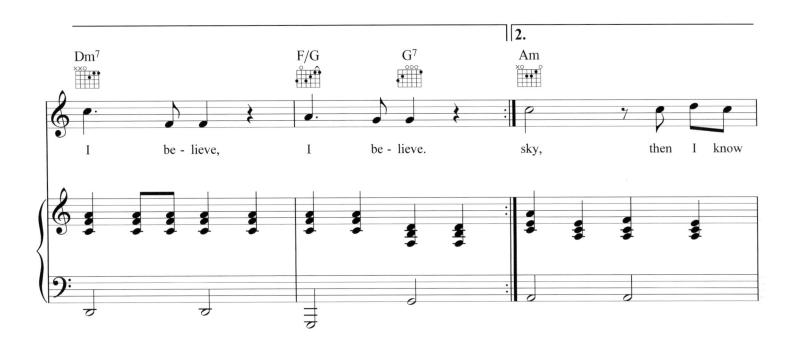

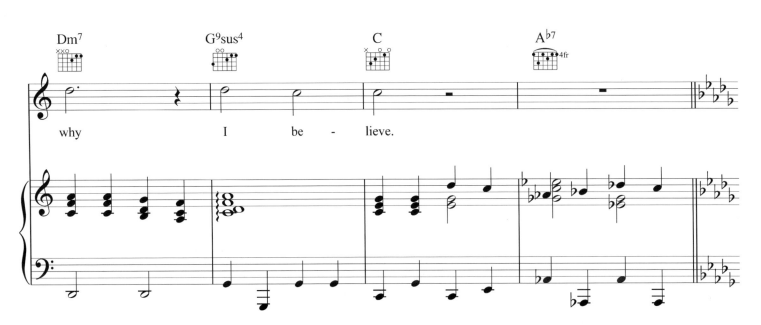

Ev - 'ry time I hear a new - born ba - by cry or touch a

leaf or see the sky, then I know why

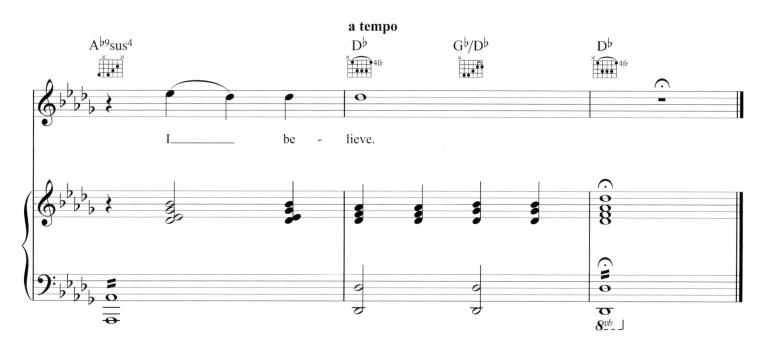

I_____ be - lieve.

I Wish I Knew How It Would Feel To Be Free

Words by Billy Taylor & Dick Dallas
Music by Billy Taylor

wish   I   knew___   how___   it would   feel_____   to be free..

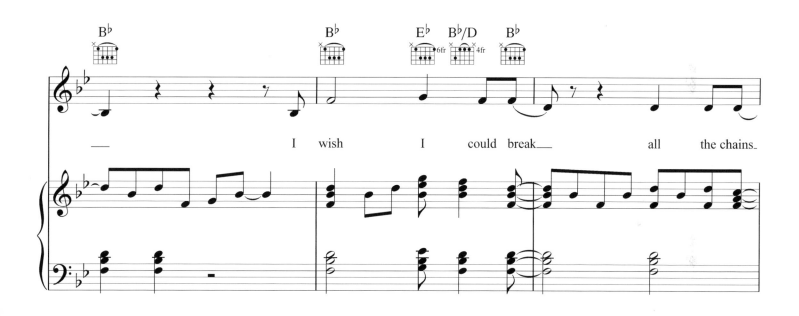

___   I wish   I could break___   all   the chains__

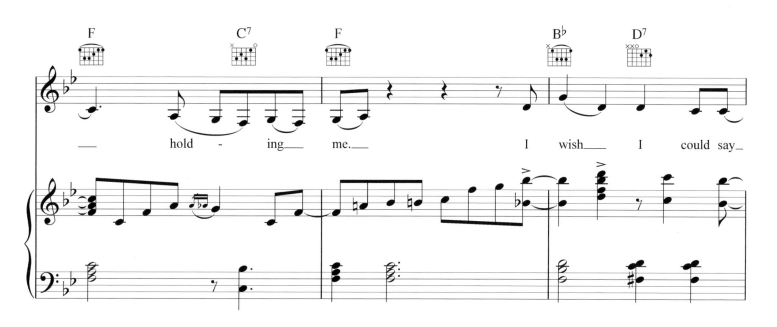

___   hold - ing___ me.___   I wish___ I could say_

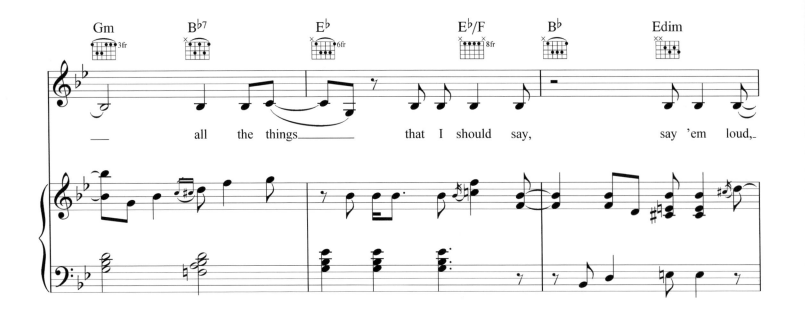

all the things _____ that I should say, say 'em loud, _

_____ say 'em _____ clear, for the whole _____ round ____ world_ to hear. _

____ I wish I could share _____ all the

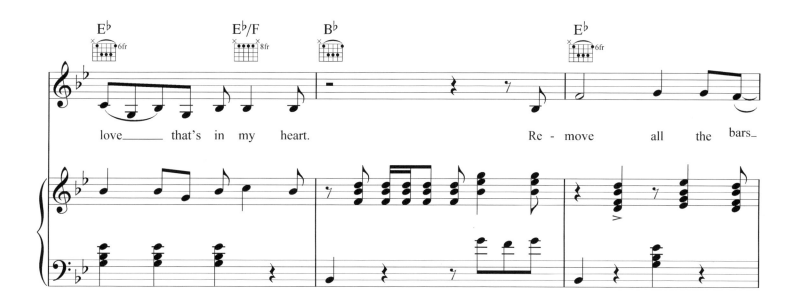

love_____ that's in my heart.   Re - move   all   the   bars_

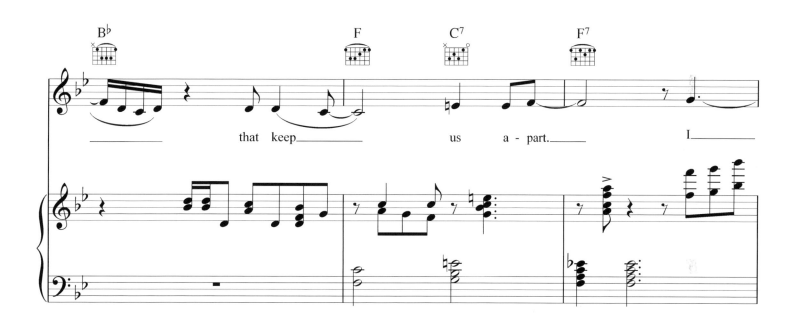

_____   that keep_____   us   a - part._____   I_____

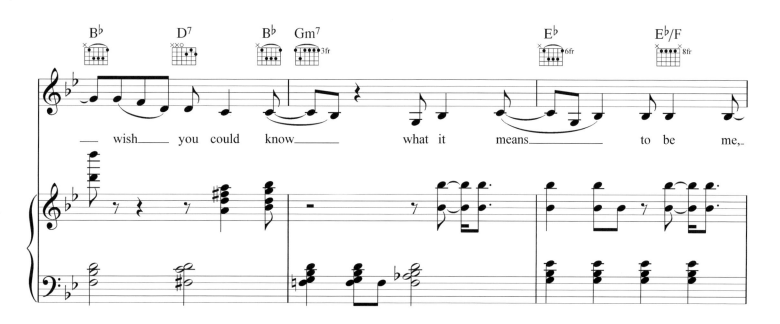

___ wish_____ you could   know_____   what it   means_____   to be   me,_

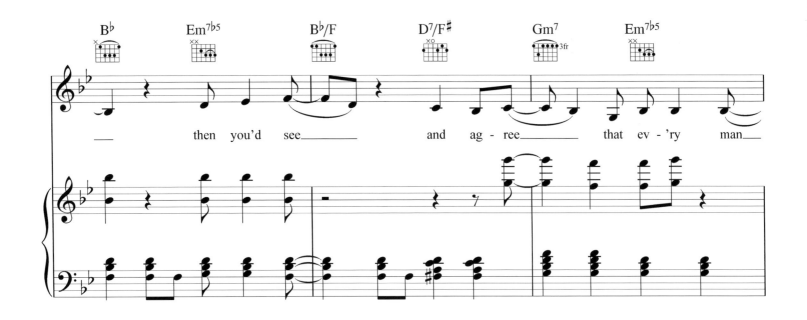

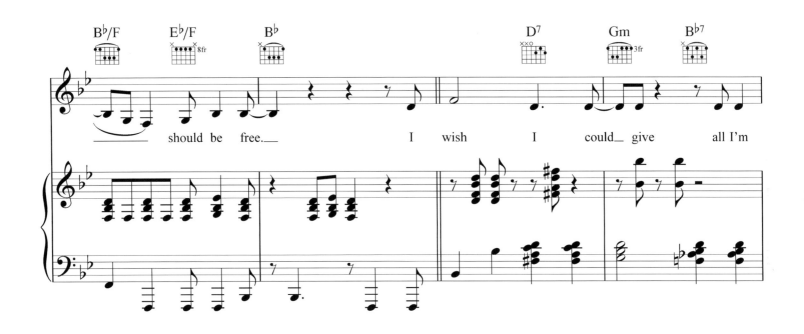

long - ing_____ to live._ I wish I___ could do___ all___ the

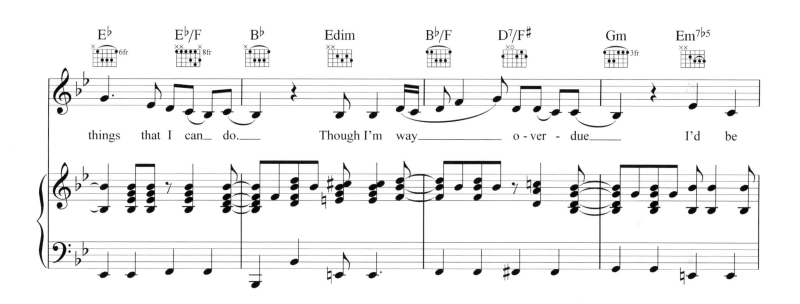

things that I can do.___ Though I'm way_____ o - ver - due___ I'd be

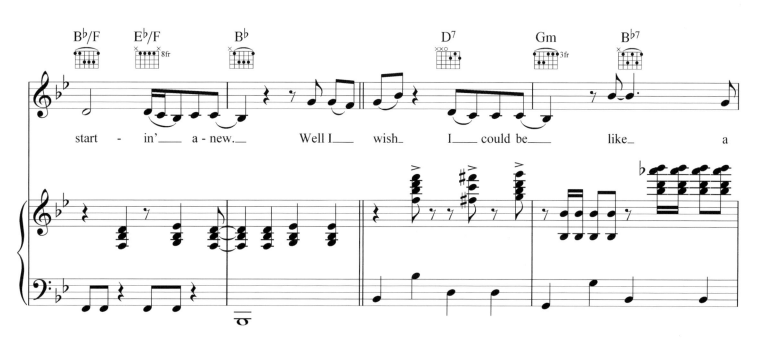

start - in'___ a - new._ Well I___ wish_ I___ could be___ like__ a

71

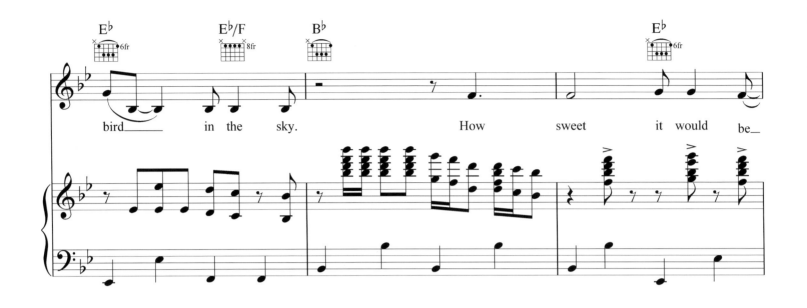

bird_____ in the sky. How sweet it would be__

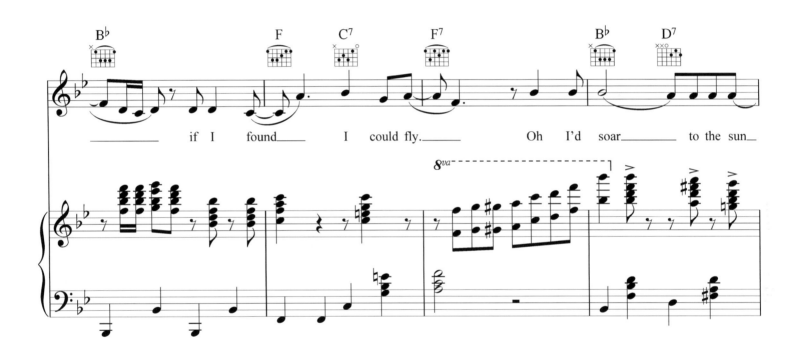

_____ if I found_____ I could fly._____ Oh I'd soar_____ to the sun__

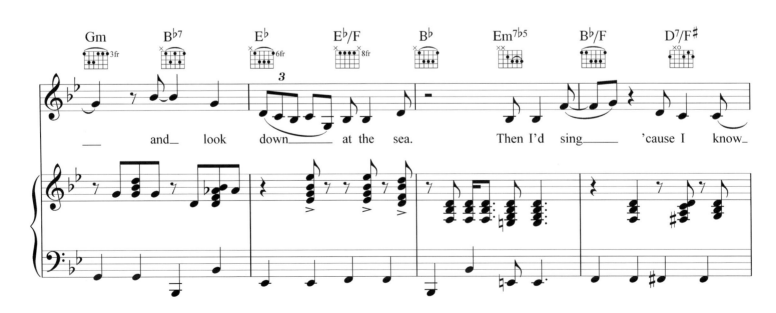

__ and__ look down_____ at the sea. Then I'd sing_____ 'cause I know__

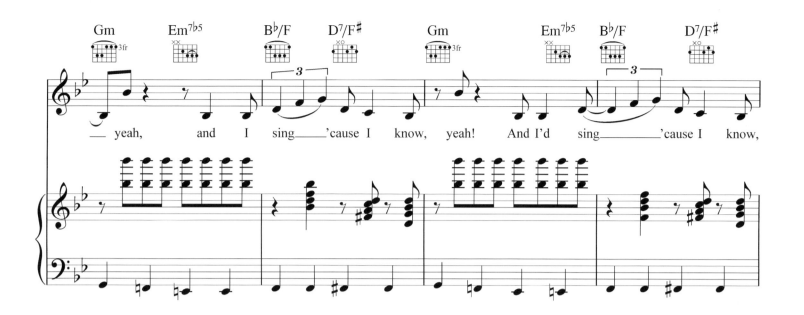

Repeat ad lib. to fade

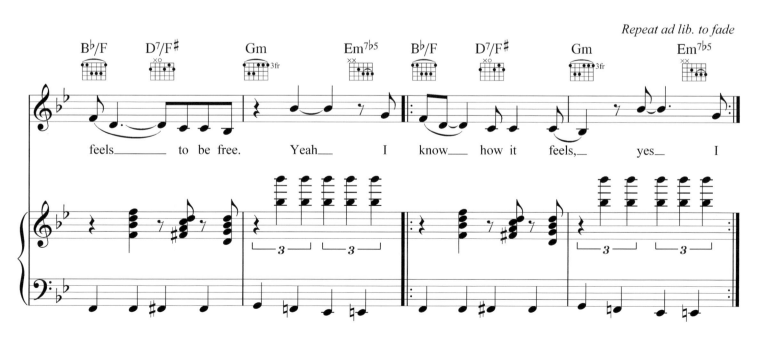

I Still Haven't Found What I'm Looking For

Words & Music by U2

Original key Db major

♩ = 104

climbed___ high - est moun - tains,___ I____ have run____ through the
(2.) kissed___ hon - ey lips,____ felt___ the heal - ing in her fin - ger
(3.) -lieve in the king - dom come____ then all the co - lours will bleed in - to

fields on - ly___ to be with___ you,____ on - ly____ to
tips, it burned___ like fire,____ I was burn - ing,___ in -
one, bleed in - to one,____ but___ yes I'm still

be with___ you.____ I____ have run,___ I have
-side her.____ I____ have spoke___ with the tongue of
run - ning.____ You broke___ the bonds and you loosed the

crawled, I____ have scaled___ these___ cit - y walls,____ these___ cit - y
an - gels, I____ have held the hand___ of a dev - il, it was warm in the
chains, car - ried the cross___ of my shame, oh, my

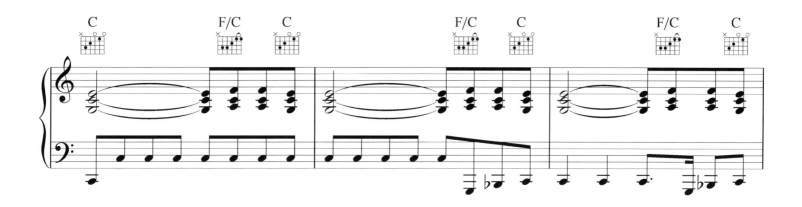

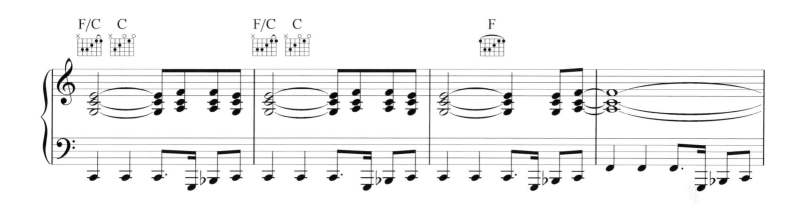

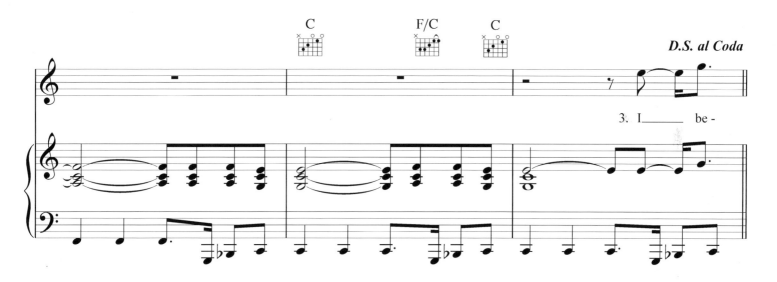

D.S. al Coda

3. I_____ be -

⊕ Coda

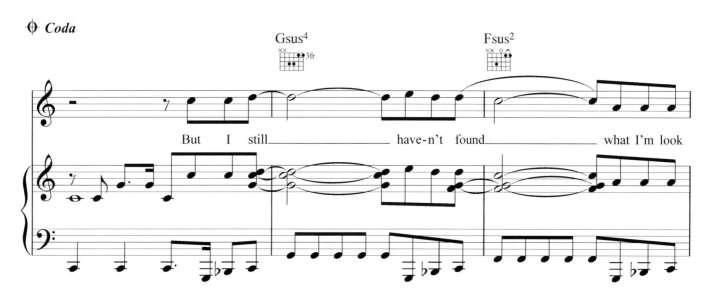

But   I   still_____ have-n't found_____ what I'm look

ing for._____ But I still_____ have-n't found__

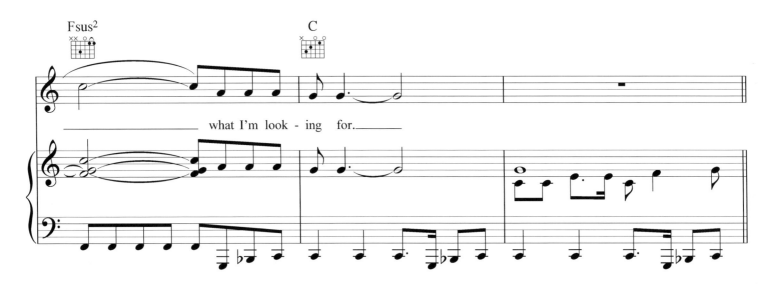

_____ what I'm look - ing for._____

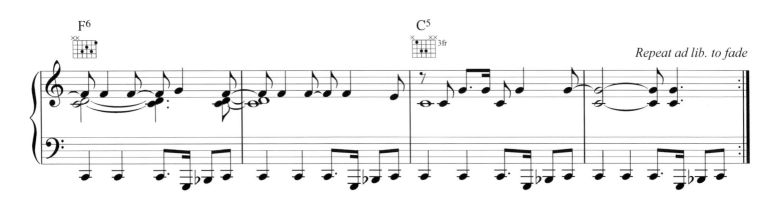

If I Can Dream

Words & Music by W. Earl Brown

soul_ and fly._____

Deep in my

heart_____ there's a trem - bling ques - tion.

Still I am

sure_____ that the ans-wer's, ans-wer's gon-na come some - how. Out there in the

dark there's a beck-on-ing can - dle,_____ and while I can

JOHN LENNON

Imagine

Words & Music by John Lennon

1. I-ma-gine there's no hea-ven, it's ea-sy if you try.___

No hell___ be-low us,___ a-bove us on-ly sky.

you may say___ I'm a dream-er, but I'm not the on - ly one.___

I hope some day___ you'll join us,___ and the world___ will be as one..

I-ma-gine no__ pos-es - sions, I won-der if you can.___

No need for greed or hun - ger, a bro-ther-hood__ of man.___

The Impossible Dream
(from 'Man Of La Mancha')

Words by Joe Darion
Music by Mitch Leigh

pause, to be will- ing to march in- to Hell for a hea- ven- ly cause. And I

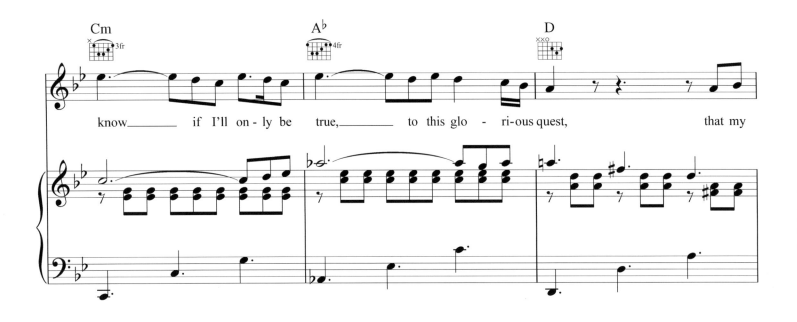

know_____ if I'll on - ly be true,_____ to this glo - ri- ous quest, that my

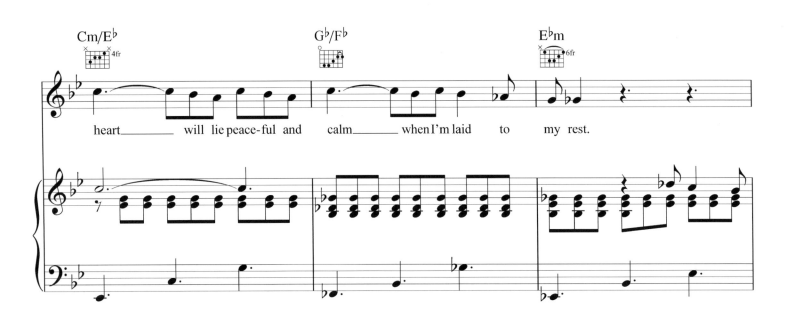

heart_____ will lie peace- ful and calm_____ when I'm laid to my rest.

3. And the world_____ will be bet-ter for this, that one

man,_____ scorned___ and cov-ered with scars,_____ still___

strove_____ with his last ounce of cour- age,_____ to

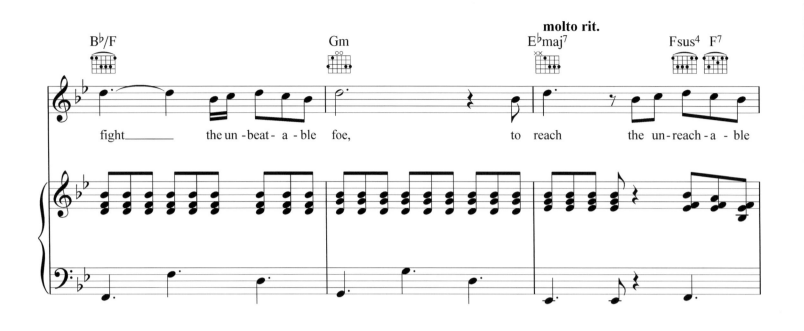

fight_____ the un-beat-a-ble foe, to reach the un-reach-a-ble

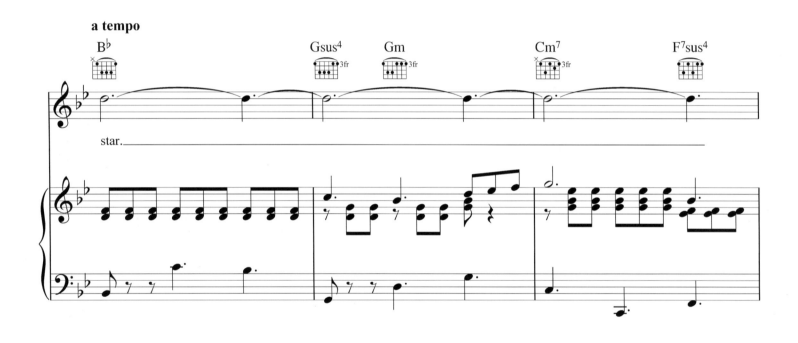

star._____

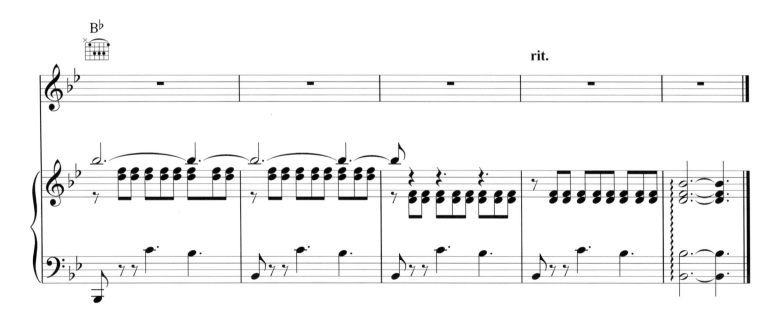

Lost

Words & Music by Michael Buble, Alan Chang & Jann Richards

Original key B major

♩ = 70

1. I can't be - lieve it's o - ver,_____ I watched the whole thing fall, and I
2. Sum - mer turned to win - ter, and the snow it turned to rain, then the
3. Life can show no mer - cy, it can tear your soul a - part; it can

To Coda 1 ⊕

Lean On Me

Words & Music by Bill Withers

99

THE BEATLES

Let It Be

Words & Music by John Lennon & Paul McCartney

1. When I find my-self_ in times_ of trou-ble Moth-er Ma-ry comes_ to me,

speak - ing words of wis - dom, let it be._____ And

guitar solo ad lib.

Let it be,

let it be, let it be, yeah, let it be.

106

Love Can Build A Bridge

Words & Music by John Jarvis, Paul Overstreet & Naomi Judd

share with you___ the last___ bite_____ of bread I had___ to eat. I would
love and on - ly love_____ can join___ the tribes_ of man. I would

swim out___ to save you___ in your sea of bro - ken dreams,_____ when
give my heart's de - si - re____ that you__ might see_____ the

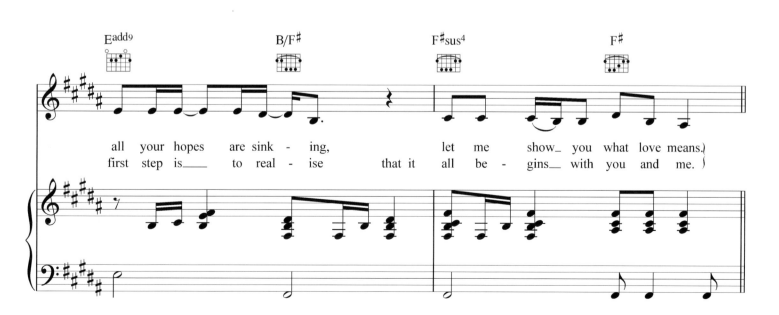

all your hopes are sink - ing, let me show_ you what love means.)
first step is__ to real - ise that it all be - gins__ with you and me.)

2. I would

Don't you think it's time?

When we stand to-geth-er it's our fin-est hour. We can do

111

112

Many Rivers To Cross

Words & Music by Jimmy Cliff

Wan - der - ing, I am lost_____ as I trav - el a - long_____
times I find my - self_____ think-ing of_____ com - mit - ting_____

the white____ cliffs of____ Dov - er.
some_____ dread - ful____ crime.   Yes, I've got

Man - y riv-ers to cross_____ and it's on - ly my will____ that____ keeps me a-
man - y riv-ers to cross_____ but I can't seem to find____ my____ way ov-

-live.   I've been licked, washed up for years_____
- er.   2° fade to end   Wan - der-ing, I am lost

114

Morning Has Broken

Words by Eleanor Farjeon

God's re- cre- a- tion of the new day.

No Matter What
(from 'Whistle Down The Wind')

Music by Andrew Lloyd Webber
Lyrics by Jim Steinman

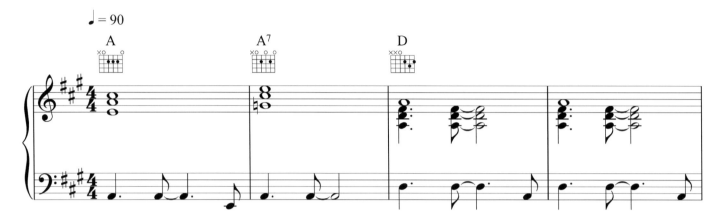

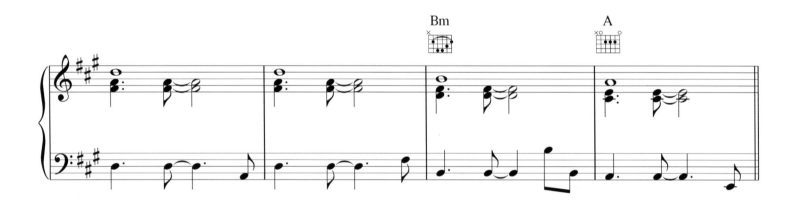

1. No mat-ter what they tell us, no mat-ter what they do,
2. If on-ly tears were laugh-ter, if on-ly night was day,

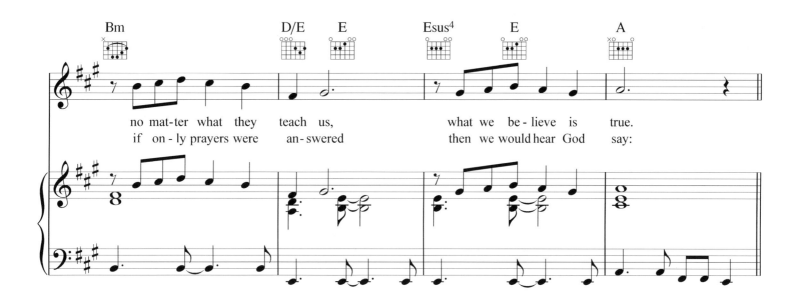

no mat-ter what they teach us, what we be-lieve is true.
if on-ly prayers were an-swered then we would hear God say:

No mat-ter what they call us, how-ev-er they at-
No mat-ter what they tell you, no mat-ter what they

- tack, no mat-ter where they take us,
do, no mat-ter what they teach you,

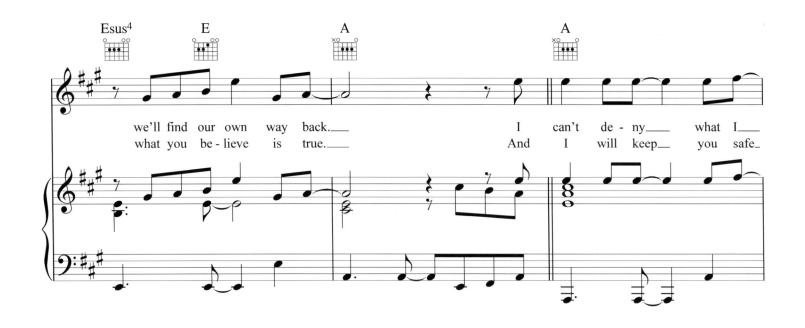

we'll find our own way back.___

I can't de - ny___ what I___
what you be - lieve is true.___

And I will keep__ you safe_

___ be - lieve,___

I can't be__ what I'm not.___
___ and strong_

and shel - tered__ from the storm.___

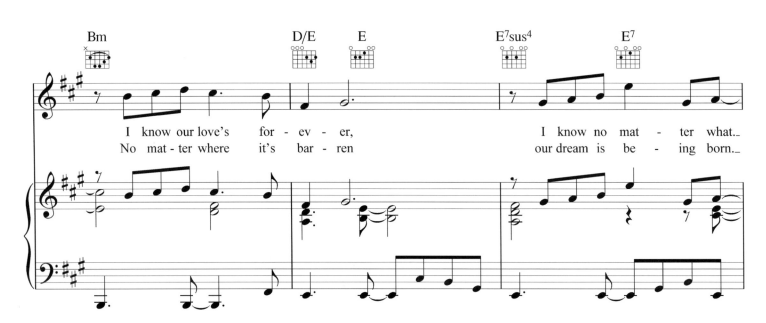

I know our love's for - ev - er,

I know no mat - ter what__
No mat - ter where it's bar - ren

our dream is be - ing born.__

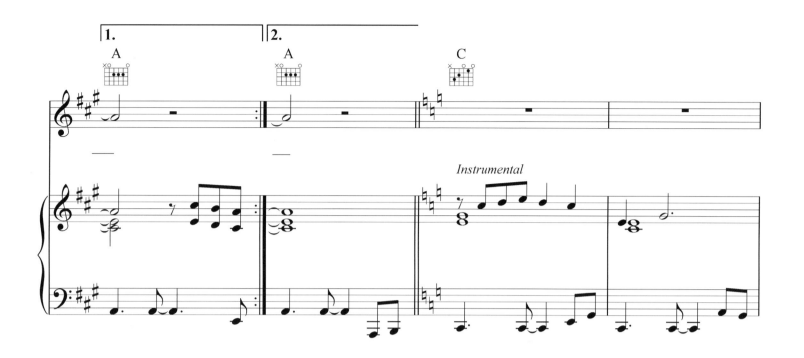

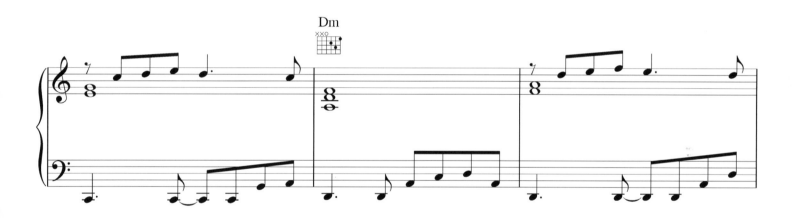

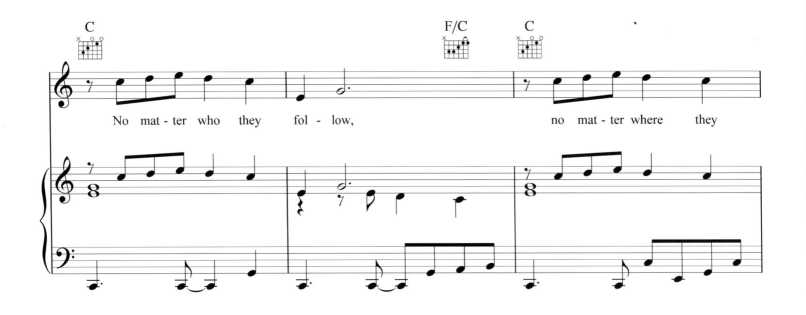

No mat-ter who they fol-low, no mat-ter where they

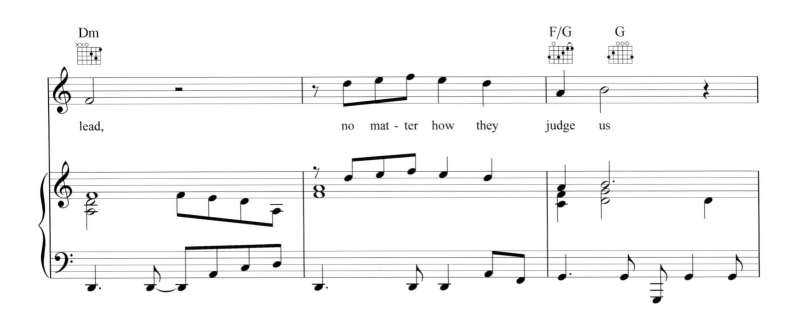

lead, no mat-ter how they judge us

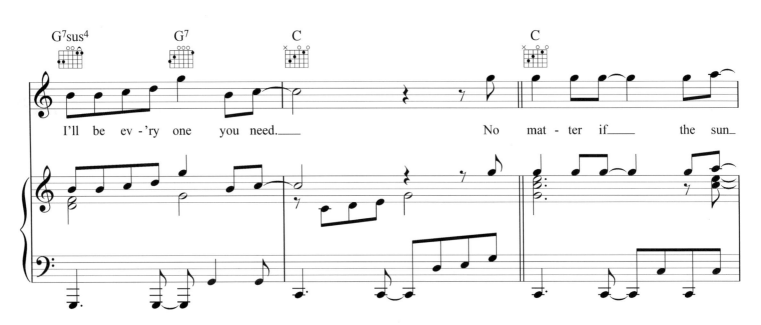

I'll be ev-'ry one you need.___ No mat-ter if___ the sun___

don't shine,___ or if the___ skies are blue.___

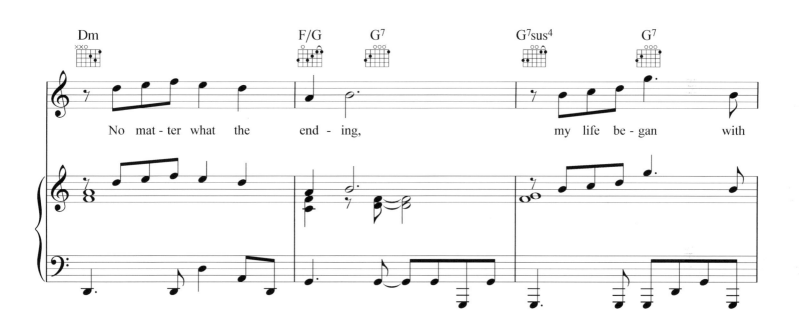

No mat-ter what the end-ing, my life be-gan with

you. I can't de-ny___ what I___ be-lieve,___

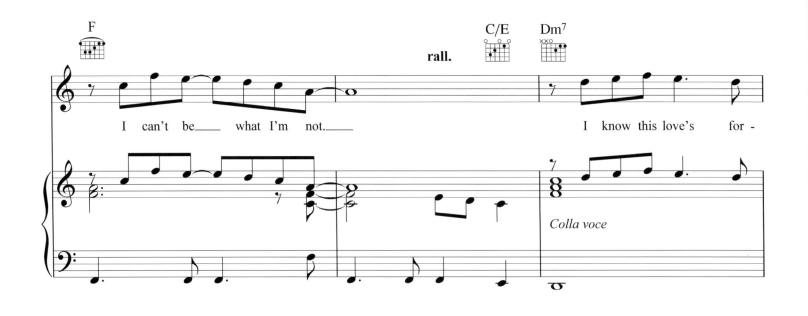

I can't be____ what I'm not.____   I know this love's for -

- ev - er,   That all that mat - ters now no mat - ter what. No,   no

mat - ter,   no.   No,   no   mat - ter,   no.
(No no mat - ter what.)   (No no mat -)

One Love/People Get Ready

Words & Music by Bob Marley & Curtis Mayfield

One love,__ one heart.__

Let's get to-geth-er and feel all right.__

Hear the chil-dren
As it was in the be-
I'm plead-ing to____

Only Hope

Words & Music by Jonathan Foreman

Singing in all that I am, at the top of my lungs, I'm giving it back.

on - ly hope.

Hmm, hmm. Ooh.

Patience

Words & Music by Mark Owen, Gary Barlow,
Jason Orange, Howard Donald & John Shanks

Step By Step

Words & Music by Annie Lennox

147

(Something Inside) So Strong

Words & Music by Labi Siffre

1. The high-er you build your bar-ri-ers, the tall-er I be-come.
2. The more you re-fuse to hear my voice, the loud-er I will sing.

The fur-ther you take my rights a-way, the fast-er I will run.
You hide be-hind walls of Je-ri-cho, your lies will come tumb-ling.

though you're do-ing me wrong, so wrong. You thought that my pride was gone,___ oh no.___

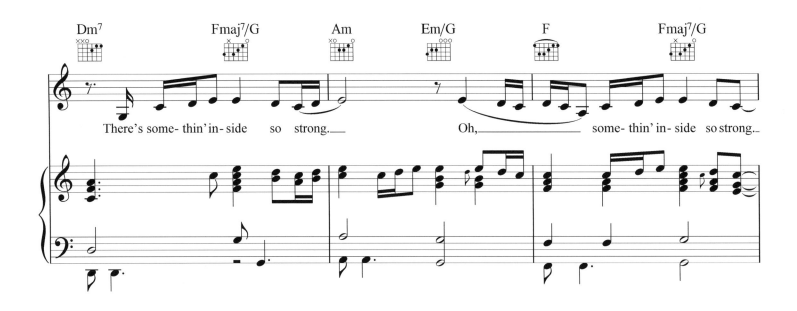

There's some-thin' in-side so strong.___ Oh,_____ some-thin' in-side so strong.___

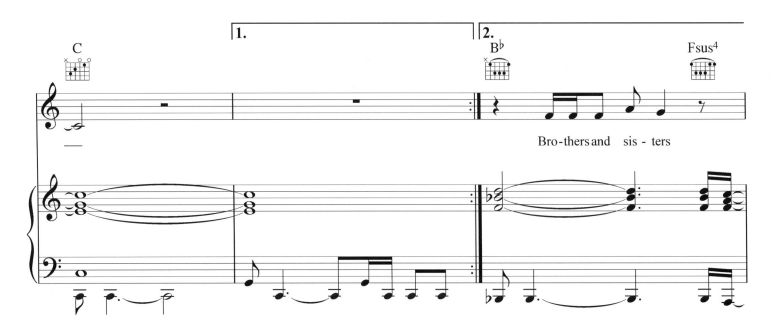

Bro-thers and sis-ters

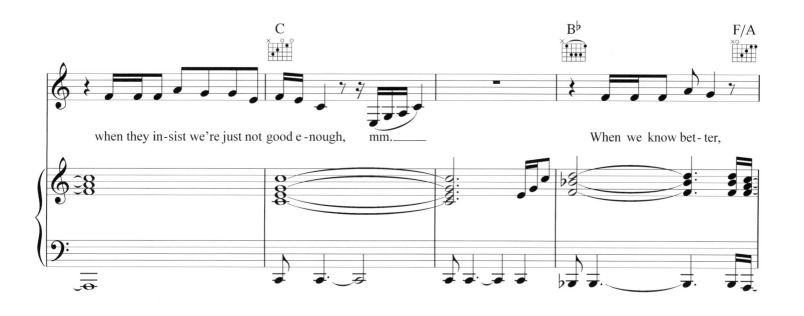

when they in-sist we're just not good e -nough,　　mm.＿＿＿　　　When we know bet- ter,

just look 'em in the eyes and say:　　"We're gon-na do it an- y - way,＿　　we're gon-na do it an- y - way."＿

We're gon-na do it an- y - way,＿　　we're gon-na do it an- y - way."＿＿＿　　Be-cause＿there's

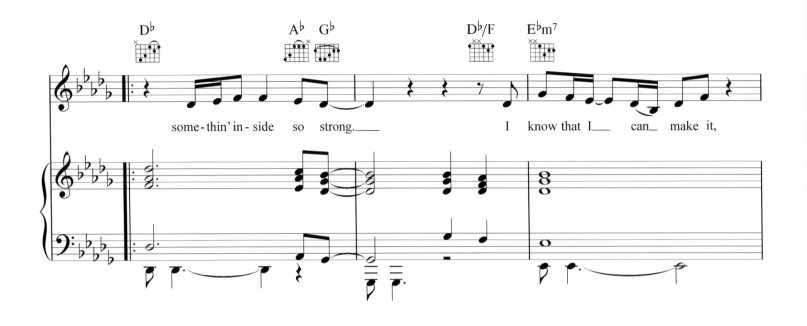

some-thin' in - side so strong.____ I know that I____ can____ make it,

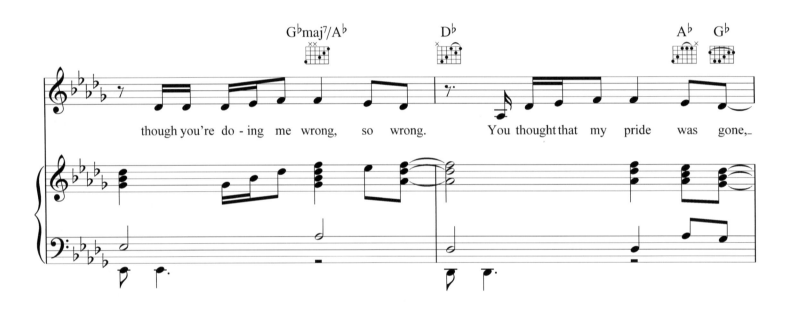

though you're do - ing me wrong, so wrong. You thought that my pride was gone,____

1.

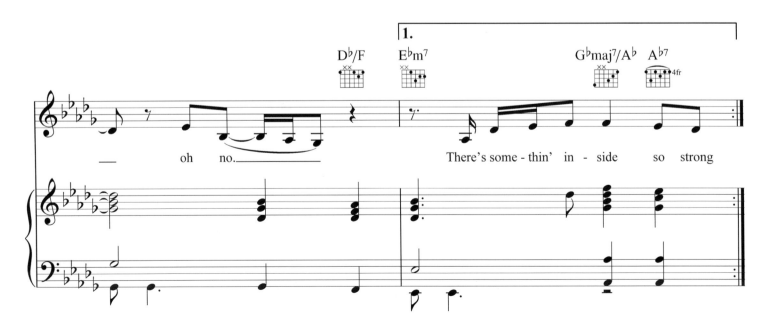

____ oh no.____ There's some - thin' in - side so strong

There's some-thin' in-side so strong.___ Oh,_____ some-thin' in-side so strong.___

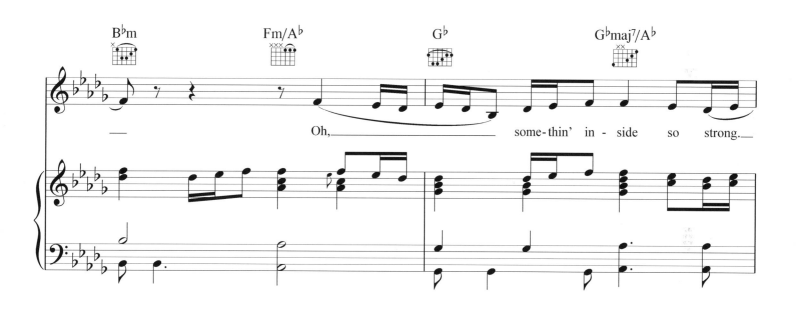

___ Oh,_____ some-thin' in - side so strong.___

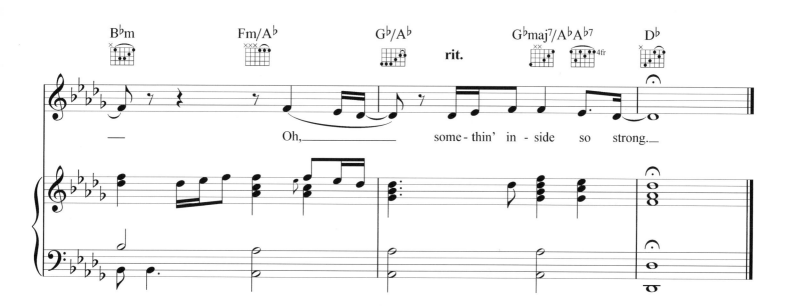

rit.

___ Oh,_____ some-thin' in - side so strong.___

Tears In Heaven

Words & Music by Eric Clapton & Will Jennings

Be-yond the door____ there's peace, I'm sure,_

Time Is A Healer

Words & Music by Diane Scanlon & Greg Smith

1. I've found a pic-ture of your_____
2. I spoke such harsh words be-fore our

smil-ing face,_____ bring-ing old_____ mem'-ries_____
good-bye. Well, I want-ed to hurt you for the

that I_____ had_____ locked a- way._____ The__ bur - den of
tears_____ you made, you made me cry. All__ my hopes and

an - ger_____ from__ a heart__ filled with pain__
dreams,__ well they start - ed van-ish - ing._____

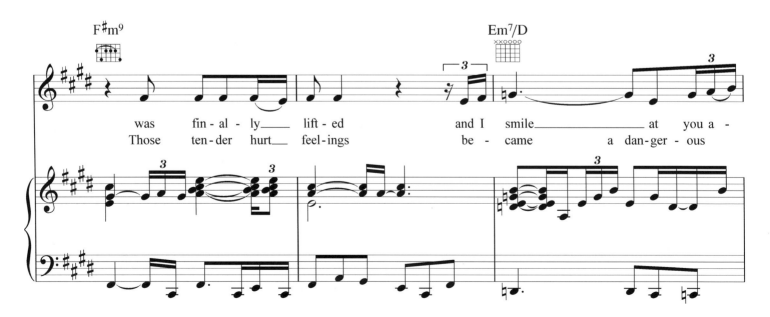

was fin - al - ly__ lift - ed and I smile_____ at you a -
Those ten-der hurt__ feel-ings be - came a dan-ger - ous

geth - er a - gain_____ 'cause love heals the wound it makes._____

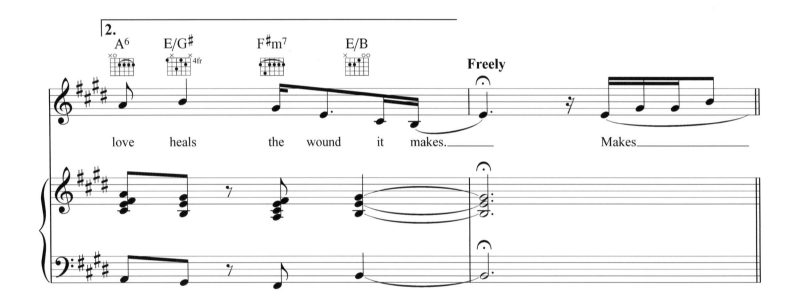

love heals the wound it makes._____ Makes_____

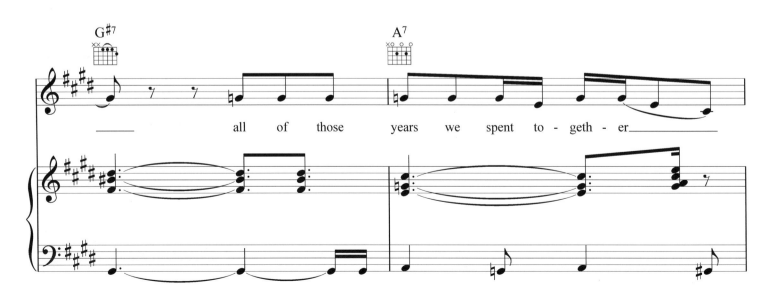

_____ all of those years we spent to - geth - er_____

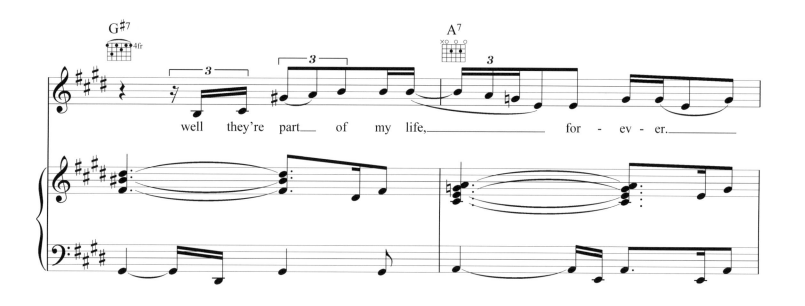

well   they're   part___   of   my   life,_____   for - ev - er._____

I   hold   the   joy____   with   the   pain_____   and   the   truth   is___

I   miss   you_____   my   friend._____

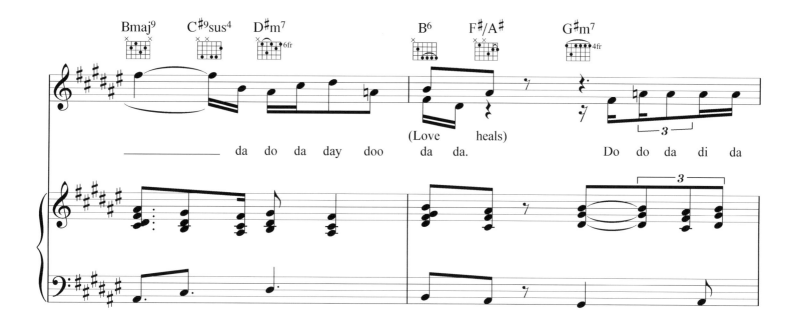

da do da day doo da da. (Love heals)

Do do da di da

do dee da do da do dow. (Love heals) The wound

colla voce

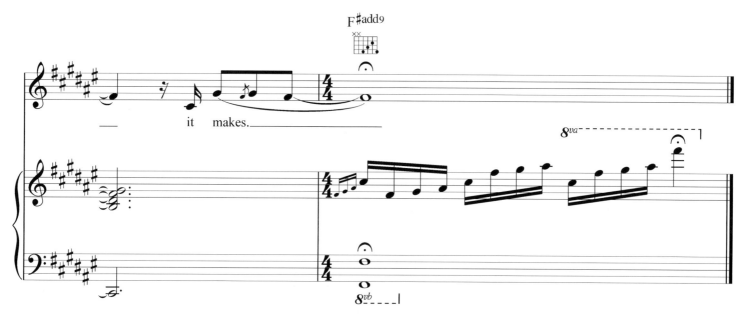

it makes.

The Voice Within

Words & Music by Christina Aguilera & Glen Ballard

167

heart - ache life can bring and__ what it means.)
look out - side, look in - side__ to your soul.)

When there's

no - one else, look in - side your- self; like your old - est friend,_____ just

trust the voice with - in.__ Then you'll find the strength_ that will guide your way if

you'll learn_ to be - gin_____ to trust the voice with - in.__

trust the voice with - in.

(Ooh, ooh,

ooh, ooh.)

Life is a jour-ney;___ it can

take you an - - y-where___ you choose to go.___   As long as you're learn-ing___ you'll find

169

What A Wonderful World

Words & Music by George Weiss & Bob Thiele

You Can Get It If You Really Want

Words & Music by Jimmy Cliff

To Coda ⊕

try, try and try, try and try. You'll suc-ceed at last.

Mmm.
Don't you know it. Yeah.

1. Per - se - cu - tion you must bear, win or lose you got - ta
2. Rome was not built in a day, op - po - si - tion will

You Gotta Be

Words by Des'ree
Music by Des'ree & Ashley Ingram

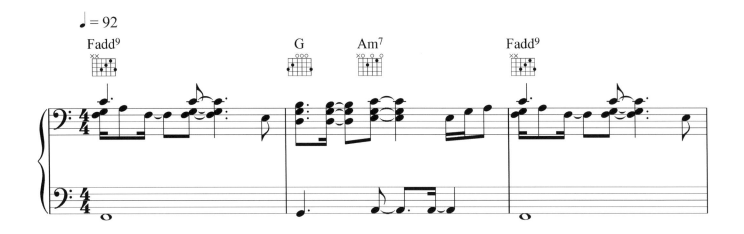

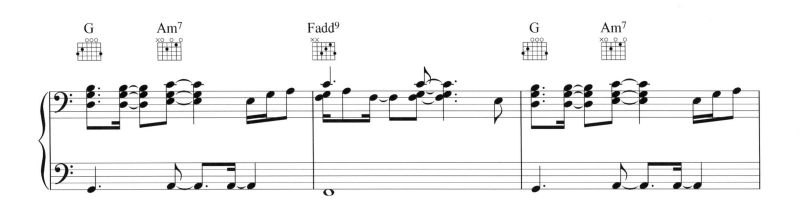

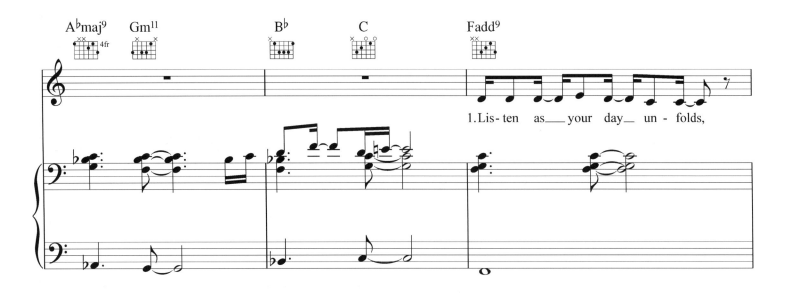

1.Lis - ten as___ your day___ un - folds,

tough, you got-ta be strong-er.___ You got-ta be cool, you got-ta be

calm, you got-ta stay to-geth-er.___ All I know, all I___ know love will save_ the day.___

2. Her-ald what___ your moth-er said,___ read the books___ your fath-er read,___
3. Lis-ten as___ your day___ un-folds, chal-lenge what___ the fu-ture holds,

try to solve_the puz-zles in_your own sweet time.___ Some may have_ more cash_ than you,
try to keep your head up to_the sky.___ Lov-ers, they_ may cause you tears,

Time asks_ no ques - tions, it goes on with- out_ you, leav - ing you_ be - hind_ if you_ can't stand_

_ the pace.____ The world keeps____ on spin - ning, can't stop it

if you_ tried____ to. The best part____ is dan - ger star - ing you_

_ in the face. Whoa._____ Re - mem - ber

D.S. al Coda

You got - ta be hard, you got - ta be tough, you got - ta be strong - er.

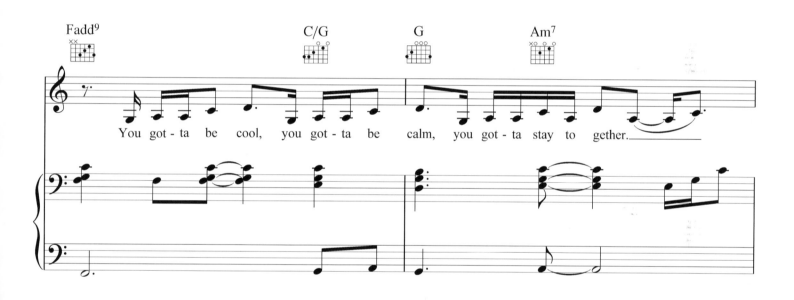

You got - ta be cool, you got - ta be calm, you got - ta stay to - gether.

Repeat ad lib to fade

All I know,__ all I__ know love will save__ the day.__

You Raise Me Up

Words & Music by Brendan Graham & Rolf Løvland

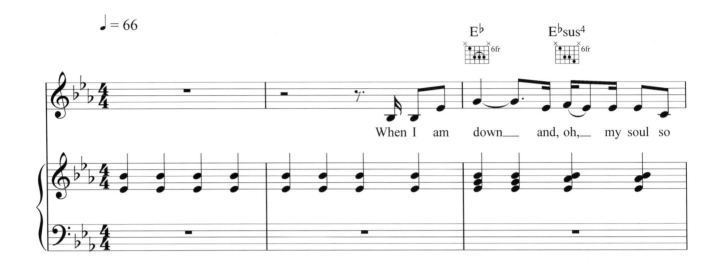

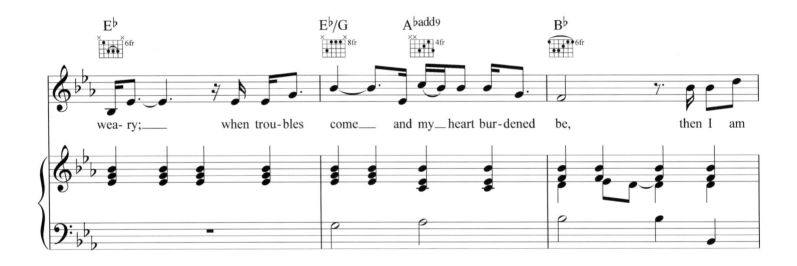

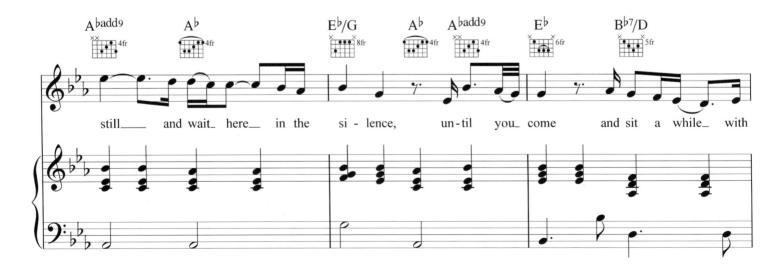